IMAGINE THAT™

Licensed exclusively to Imagine That Publishing Ltd
Tide Mill Way, Woodbridge, Suffolk, IP12 1AP, UK
www.imaginethat.com
Copyright © 2021 Imagine That Group Ltd
All rights reserved
2 4 6 8 9 7 5 3 1
Manufactured in China

Adapted by Kitty Taylor
Illustrated by Paul Nicholls

ISBN 978-1-80105-173-6

A catalogue record for this book is available from the British Library

Congratulations on a great first term in Year 1.

Happy Christmas!

Love

Miss Tenglin

We Wish You A MERRY CHRISTMAS

Adapted by
Kitty Taylor

Illustrated by
Paul Nicholls

Merry
Christmas!

We wish you a merry Christmas,
We wish you a merry Christmas,
We wish you a merry Christmas,
And a happy New Year.

Good tidings we bring
to you and your kin,
We wish you a merry Christmas
and a **happy** New Year.

Merry
Christmas!

Now bring us some figgy pudding,
Now bring us some figgy pudding,
Now bring us some figgy pudding,
And bring some out here!

It's Christmas!

Good tidings we bring
to you and your kin,

We wish you a merry Christmas
and a happy New Year.

For we all love our figgy pudding,
For we all love our figgy pudding,

Happy Christmas!

Hello there!

For we all love our figgy pudding,
And lots of good cheer!

Good tidings we bring
to you and your kin,

We wish you a merry Christmas
and a happy New Year.

And we won't go until we get some,
And we won't go until we get some,

Pudding, please!

And we won't go until we get some,
So bring some out here!

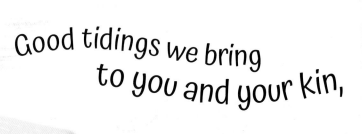

Good tidings we bring
to you and your kin,

I love
singing!

We wish you a merry Christmas
and a happy New Year.

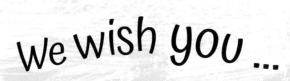

We wish you ...

... a merry Christmas ...

We wish you ...

... a merry
Christmas ...

We wish you a
merry Christmas ...

... And a **happy** New year!

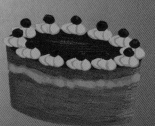